This Journal belongs to

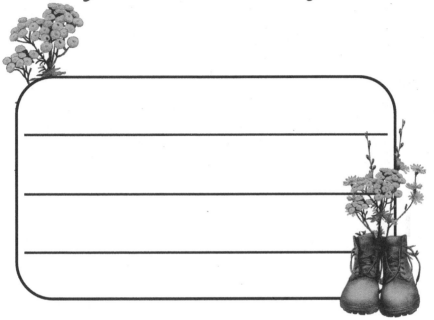

If found, please contact me at

Index

Page	Hike	Date
....	....	....
....	....	....
....	....	....
....	....	....
....	....	....
....	....	....
....	....	....
....	....	....
....	....	....
....	....	....
....	....	....
....	....	....
....	....	....
....	....	....
....	....	....
....	....	....
....	....	....
....	....	....
....	....	....
....	....	....
....	....	....
....	....	....
....	....	....
....	....	....
....	....	....
....	....	....
....	....	....
....	....	....
....	....	....
....	....	....

Index

Page	Hike	Date

Hike/Trail Name: _____

Date: _____ Start Time: _____ End Time: _____

City/State: _____ Total Distance: _____

Companions: _____

Trail Type: Loop   Out and Back   Point-to-point

Weather: ☼   ⛅   ☁   🌧   ❄

Difficulty/Grade of the Hike: (circle a grade level):

Grade–   1   2   3   4   5

Amenities: (check all that apply)

Drinking-Water   Pet Friendly   Toilets   Cell Reception   Picnic Table

Good
Average
Poor

Gear & Supplies: _____
_____

Food & Beverages: _____
_____

Observances & Sightings (Nature, views, wildlife): _____
_____
_____

Sketch/Photo/Notes

Sketch/Photo/Journal

Hike/Trail Name: _____

Date: _____ **Start Time:** _____ **End Time:** _____

City/State: _____ **Total Distance:** _____

Companions: _____

Trail Type: Loop   Out and Back   Point-to-point

Weather: ☀ ⛅ ☁ 🌧 ❄

Difficulty/Grade of the Hike: (circle a grade level):

Grade—   1   2   3   4   5

Amenities: (check all that apply)

Drinking-Water   Pet Friendly   Toilets   Cell Reception (Good / Average / Poor)   Picnic Table

Gear & Supplies: _____

_____

Food & Beverages: _____

_____

Observances & Sightings (Nature, views, wildlife): _____

_____

Sketch/Photo/Notes

Sketch/Photo/Journal

Hike/Trail Name: _____

Date: _____ **Start Time:** _____ **End Time:** _____

City/State: _____ **Total Distance:** _____

Companions: _____

Trail Type: Loop   Out and Back   Point-to-point

Weather: ☀ 🌤 ☁ 🌧 ❄

Difficulty/Grade of the Hike: (circle a grade level):

Grade—   1   2   3   4   5

Amenities: (check all that apply)

Drinking-Water   Pet Friendly   Toilets   Cell Reception (Good / Average / Poor)   Picnic Table

Gear & Supplies: _____

_____

Food & Beverages: _____

_____

Observances & Sightings (Nature, views, wildlife): _____

_____

10

Sketch/Photo/Notes

Sketch/Photo/Journal

Hike/Trail Name: _____

Date: _____   **Start Time:** _____   **End Time:** _____

City/State: _____   **Total Distance:** _____

Companions: _____

Trail Type: Loop   Out and Back   Point-to-point

Weather: ☀️   🌤️   ☁️   🌧️   ❄️

Difficulty/Grade of the Hike: (circle a grade level):

Grade—   1   2   3   4   5

Amenities: (check all that apply)

Drinking-Water   Pet Friendly   Toilets   Cell Reception   Picnic Table

Good / Average / Poor

Gear & Supplies: _____
_____

Food & Beverages: _____
_____

Observances & Sightings (Nature, views, wildlife):
_____
_____

Sketch/Photo/Notes

Sketch/Photo/Journal

Hike/Trail Name: _____

Date: _____ Start Time: _____ End Time: _____

City/State: _____ Total Distance: _____

Companions: _____

Trail Type: Loop   Out and Back   Point-to-point

Weather: ☀ 🌤 ☁ 🌧 ❄

Difficulty/Grade of the Hike: (circle a grade level):

Grade–   1   2   3   4   5

Amenities: (check all that apply)

Drinking-Water   Pet Friendly   Toilets   Cell Reception (Good / Average / Poor)   Picnic Table

Gear & Supplies: _____
_____

Food & Beverages: _____
_____

Observances & Sightings (Nature, views, wildlife): _____
_____
_____

Sketch/Photo/Notes

Sketch/Photo/Journal

Hike/Trail Name: _____

Date: _____ **Start Time:** _____ **End Time:** _____

City/State: _____ **Total Distance:** _____

Companions: _____

Trail Type: Loop   Out and Back   Point-to-point

Weather: ☀️ 🌤️ ☁️ 🌧️ ❄️

Difficulty/Grade of the Hike: (circle a grade level):

Grade—   1   2   3   4   5

Amenities: (check all that apply)

Drinking-Water   Pet Friendly   Toilets   Cell Reception (Good / Average / Poor)   Picnic Table

Gear & Supplies: _____

Food & Beverages: _____

Observances & Sightings (Nature, views, wildlife): _____

Sketch/Photo/Notes

Sketch/Photo/Journal

Hike/Trail Name: _____

Date: _____ **Start Time:** _____ **End Time:** _____

City/State: _____ **Total Distance:** _____

Companions: _____

Trail Type: Loop   Out and Back   Point-to-point

Weather: ☼   ⛅   ☁   🌧   ❄

Difficulty/Grade of the Hike: (circle a grade level):

Grade—   1   2   3   4   5

Amenities: (check all that apply)

Drinking-Water   Pet Friendly   Toilets   Cell Reception (Good / Average / Poor)   Picnic Table

Gear & Supplies: _____

Food & Beverages: _____

Observances & Sightings (Nature, views, wildlife): _____

Sketch/Photo/Notes

Sketch/Photo/Journal

Hike/Trail Name: _____

Date: _____   **Start Time:** _____   **End Time:** _____

City/State: _____   **Total Distance:** _____

Companions: _____

Trail Type: Loop   Out and Back   Point-to-point

Weather: ☀ ⛅ ☁ 🌧 ❄

Difficulty/Grade of the Hike: (circle a grade level):

Grade—   1   2   3   4   5

Amenities: (check all that apply)

Drinking-Water   Pet Friendly   Toilets   Cell Reception   Picnic Table

Good
Average
Poor

Gear & Supplies: _____
_____

Food & Beverages: _____
_____

Observances & Sightings (Nature, views, wildlife):
_____
_____

Sketch/Photo/Notes

Sketch/Photo/Journal

Hike/Trail Name: _____

Date: _____ **Start Time:** _____ **End Time:** _____

City/State: _____ **Total Distance:** _____

Companions: _____

Trail Type: Loop   Out and Back   Point-to-point

Weather: ☀   🌤   ☁   🌧   ❄

Difficulty/Grade of the Hike: (circle a grade level):

Grade–   1   2   3   4   5

Amenities: (check all that apply)

Drinking-Water   Pet Friendly   Toilets   Cell Reception (Good / Average / Poor)   Picnic Table

Gear & Supplies: _____

Food & Beverages: _____

Observances & Sightings (Nature, views, wildlife): _____

Sketch/Photo/Notes

Sketch/Photo/Journal

Hike/Trail Name: _____

Date: _____ **Start Time:** _____ **End Time:** _____

City/State: _____ **Total Distance:** _____

Companions: _____

Trail Type: Loop   Out and Back   Point-to-point

Weather: ☀ 🌤 ☁ 🌧 ❄

Difficulty/Grade of the Hike: (circle a grade level):

Grade—   1   2   3   4   5

Amenities: (check all that apply)

Drinking-Water   Pet Friendly   Toilets   Cell Reception (Good / Average / Poor)   Picnic Table

Gear & Supplies: _____

Food & Beverages: _____

Observances & Sightings (Nature, views, wildlife): _____

Sketch/Photo/Notes

Sketch/Photo/Journal

Hike/Trail Name: _____

Date: _____ **Start Time:** _____ **End Time:** _____

City/State: _____ **Total Distance:** _____

Companions: _____

Trail Type: Loop   Out and Back   Point-to-point

Weather: ☀️ 🌤️ ☁️ 🌧️ ❄️

Difficulty/Grade of the Hike: (circle a grade level):

Grade—   1   2   3   4   5

Amenities: (check all that apply)

Drinking-Water   Pet Friendly   Toilets   Cell Reception (Good / Average / Poor)   Picnic Table

Gear & Supplies: _____

_____

Food & Beverages: _____

_____

Observances & Sightings (Nature, views, wildlife): _____

_____

Sketch/Photo/Notes

Sketch/Photo/Journal

Hike/Trail Name: _____

Date: _____   **Start Time:** _____   **End Time:** _____

City/State: _____   **Total Distance:** _____

Companions: _____

Trail Type: Loop   Out and Back   Point-to-point

Weather: ☀   ⛅   ☁   🌧   ❄

Difficulty/Grade of the Hike: (circle a grade level):

Grade—   1   2   3   4   5

Amenities: (check all that apply)

Drinking-Water   Pet Friendly   Toilets   Cell Reception (Good / Average / Poor)   Picnic Table

Gear & Supplies: _____
_____

Food & Beverages: _____
_____

Observances & Sightings (Nature, views, wildlife): _____
_____

Sketch/Photo/Notes

Sketch/Photo/Journal

Hike/Trail Name: _____

Date: _____ Start Time: _____ End Time: _____

City/State: _____ Total Distance: _____

Companions: _____

Trail Type: Loop Out and Back Point-to-point

Weather: ☀ 🌤 ☁ 🌧 ❄

Difficulty/Grade of the Hike: (circle a grade level):

Grade— 1 2 3 4 5

Amenities: (check all that apply)

Drinking-Water   Pet Friendly   Toilets   Cell Reception (Good / Average / Poor)   Picnic Table

Gear & Supplies: _____

Food & Beverages: _____

Observances & Sightings (Nature, views, wildlife): _____

Sketch/Photo/Notes

Sketch/Photo/Journal

Hike/Trail Name: _____

Date: _____ **Start Time:** _____ **End Time:** _____

City/State: _____ **Total Distance:** _____

Companions: _____

Trail Type: Loop   Out and Back   Point-to-point

Weather: ☀ ⛅ ☁ 🌧 ❄

Difficulty/Grade of the Hike: (circle a grade level):

Grade—   1   2   3   4   5

Amenities: (check all that apply)

Drinking-Water   Pet Friendly   Toilets   Cell Reception (Good / Average / Poor)   Picnic Table

Gear & Supplies: _____
_____

Food & Beverages: _____
_____

Observances & Sightings (Nature, views, wildlife): _____
_____

Sketch/Photo/Notes

Sketch/Photo/Journal

Hike/Trail Name: _____

Date: _____   Start Time: _____   End Time: _____

City/State: _____   Total Distance: _____

Companions: _____

Trail Type: Loop   Out and Back   Point-to-point

Weather: ☀ 🌤 ☁ 🌧 ❄

Difficulty/Grade of the Hike: (circle a grade level):

Grade–   1   2   3   4   5

Amenities: (check all that apply)

Drinking-Water   Pet Friendly   Toilets   Cell Reception (Good / Average / Poor)   Picnic Table

Gear & Supplies: _____

_____

Food & Beverages: _____

_____

Observances & Sightings (Nature, views, wildlife): _____

_____

_____

Sketch/Photo/Notes

Sketch/Photo/Journal

Hike/Trail Name: _____

Date: _____ **Start Time:** _____ **End Time:** _____

City/State: _____ **Total Distance:** _____

Companions: _____

Trail Type: Loop   Out and Back   Point-to-point

Weather: ☀   🌤   ☁   🌧   ❄

Difficulty/Grade of the Hike: (circle a grade level):

Grade—   1   2   3   4   5

Amenities: (check all that apply)

Drinking-Water   Pet Friendly   Toilets   Cell Reception (Good / Average / Poor)   Picnic Table

Gear & Supplies: _____
_____

Food & Beverages: _____
_____

Observances & Sightings (Nature, views, wildlife):
_____
_____

Sketch/Photo/Notes

Sketch/Photo/Journal

Hike/Trail Name: _____

Date: _____ Start Time: _____ End Time: _____

City/State: _____ Total Distance: _____

Companions: _____

Trail Type: Loop   Out and Back   Point-to-point

Weather: ☼ ⛅ ☁ 🌧 ❄

Difficulty/Grade of the Hike: (circle a grade level):

Grade—   1   2   3   4   5

Amenities: (check all that apply)

Drinking-Water   Pet Friendly   Toilets   Cell Reception   Good / Average / Poor   Picnic Table

Gear & Supplies: _____

Food & Beverages: _____

Observances & Sightings (Nature, views, wildlife): _____

Sketch/Photo/Notes

Sketch/Photo/Journal

Hike/Trail Name: _____

Date: _____ **Start Time:** _____ **End Time:** _____

City/State: _____ **Total Distance:** _____

Companions: _____

Trail Type: Loop   Out and Back   Point-to-point

Weather: ☀ 🌤 ☁ 🌧 ❄

Difficulty/Grade of the Hike: (circle a grade level):

Grade–   1   2   3   4   5

Amenities: (check all that apply)

Drinking-Water   Pet Friendly   Toilets   Cell Reception (Good / Average / Poor)   Picnic Table

Gear & Supplies: _____
_____

Food & Beverages: _____
_____

Observances & Sightings (Nature, views, wildlife):
_____
_____

Sketch/Photo/Notes

Sketch/Photo/Journal

Hike/Trail Name: _____

Date: _____   Start Time: _____   End Time: _____

City/State: _____   Total Distance: _____

Companions: _____

Trail Type: Loop   Out and Back   Point-to-point

Weather: ☀ ⛅ ☁ 🌧 ❄

Difficulty/Grade of the Hike: (circle a grade level):

Grade–   1   2   3   4   5

Amenities: (check all that apply)

Drinking-Water   Pet Friendly   Toilets   Cell Reception (Good / Average / Poor)   Picnic Table

Gear & Supplies: _____

_____

Food & Beverages: _____

_____

Observances & Sightings (Nature, views, wildlife): _____

_____

_____

Sketch/Photo/Notes

Sketch/Photo/Journal

Hike/Trail Name: _____

Date: _____   **Start Time:** _____   **End Time:** _____

City/State: _____   **Total Distance:** _____

Companions: _____

Trail Type: Loop   Out and Back   Point-to-point

Weather: ☀ ⛅ ☁ 🌧 ❄

Difficulty/Grade of the Hike: (circle a grade level):

Grade–   1   2   3   4   5

Amenities: (check all that apply)

Drinking-Water   Pet Friendly   Toilets   Cell Reception   Picnic Table

Good
Average
Poor

Gear & Supplies: _____

_____

Food & Beverages: _____

_____

Observances & Sightings (Nature, views, wildlife):

_____

_____

Sketch/Photo/Notes

Sketch/Photo/Journal

Hike/Trail Name: _____

Date: _____ Start Time: _____ End Time: _____

City/State: _____ Total Distance: _____

Companions: _____

Trail Type: Loop   Out and Back   Point-to-point

Weather: ☀ 🌤 ☁ 🌧 ❄

Difficulty/Grade of the Hike: (circle a grade level):

Grade—   1   2   3   4   5

Amenities: (check all that apply)

Drinking-Water   Pet Friendly   Toilets   Cell Reception (Good / Average / Poor)   Picnic Table

Gear & Supplies: _____

_____

Food & Beverages: _____

_____

Observances & Sightings (Nature, views, wildlife): _____

_____

_____

Sketch/Photo/Notes

Sketch/Photo/Journal

Hike/Trail Name: _____

Date: _____ **Start Time:** _____ **End Time:** _____

City/State: _____ **Total Distance:** _____

Companions: _____

Trail Type: Loop   Out and Back   Point-to-point

Weather: ☀ ⛅ ☁ 🌧 ❄

Difficulty/Grade of the Hike: (circle a grade level):

Grade—   1   2   3   4   5

Amenities: (check all that apply)

Drinking-Water   Pet Friendly   Toilets   Cell Reception (Good / Average / Poor)   Picnic Table

Gear & Supplies: _____

Food & Beverages: _____

Observances & Sightings (Nature, views, wildlife): _____

Sketch/Photo/Notes

Sketch/Photo/Journal

Hike/Trail Name: _____

Date: _____ **Start Time:** _____ **End Time:** _____

City/State: _____ **Total Distance:** _____

Companions: _____

Trail Type: Loop Out and Back Point-to-point

Weather: ☀ ⛅ ☁ 🌧 ❄

Difficulty/Grade of the Hike: (circle a grade level):

Grade– 1 2 3 4 5

Amenities: (check all that apply)

Drinking-Water   Pet Friendly   Toilets   Cell Reception   Good Average Poor   Picnic Table

Gear & Supplies: _____

Food & Beverages: _____

Observances & Sightings (Nature, views, wildlife): _____

Sketch/Photo/Notes

Sketch/Photo/Journal

Hike/Trail Name: _____

Date: _____ **Start Time:** _____ **End Time:** _____

City/State: _____ **Total Distance:** _____

Companions: _____

Trail Type: Loop   Out and Back   Point-to-point

Weather: ☀   ⛅   ☁   🌧   ❄

Difficulty/Grade of the Hike: (circle a grade level):

Grade—   1   2   3   4   5

Amenities: (check all that apply)

Drinking-Water   Pet Friendly   Toilets   Cell Reception   Good / Average / Poor   Picnic Table

Gear & Supplies: _____
_____

Food & Beverages: _____
_____

Observances & Sightings (Nature, views, wildlife): _____
_____

Sketch/Photo/Notes

Sketch/Photo/Journal

Hike/Trail Name: _____

Date: _____   Start Time: _____   End Time: _____

City/State: _____   Total Distance: _____

Companions: _____

Trail Type: Loop   Out and Back   Point-to-point

Weather: ☀ ⛅ ☁ 🌧 ❄

Difficulty/Grade of the Hike: (circle a grade level):

Grade—   1   2   3   4   5

Amenities: (check all that apply)

Drinking-Water   Pet Friendly   Toilets   Cell Reception (Good / Average / Poor)   Picnic Table

Gear & Supplies: _____

Food & Beverages: _____

Observances & Sightings (Nature, views, wildlife): _____

Sketch/Photo/Notes

Sketch/Photo/Journal

Hike/Trail Name: _____

Date: _____   **Start Time:** _____   **End Time:** _____

City/State: _____   **Total Distance:** _____

Companions: _____

Trail Type: Loop   Out and Back   Point-to-point

Weather: ☀ 🌤 ☁ 🌧 ❄

Difficulty/Grade of the Hike: (circle a grade level):

Grade—   1   2   3   4   5

Amenities: (check all that apply)

Drinking-Water   Pet Friendly   Toilets   Cell Reception (Good / Average / Poor)   Picnic Table

Gear & Supplies: _____

Food & Beverages: _____

Observances & Sightings (Nature, views, wildlife): _____

Sketch/Photo/Notes

Sketch/Photo/Journal

Hike/Trail Name: _____

Date: _____ *Start Time:* _____ *End Time:* _____

City/State: _____ *Total Distance:* _____

Companions: _____

Trail Type: Loop   Out and Back   Point-to-point

Weather: ☀ 🌤 ☁ 🌧 ❄

Difficulty/Grade of the Hike: (circle a grade level):

Grade—   1   2   3   4   5

Amenities: (check all that apply)

Drinking-Water   Pet Friendly   Toilets   Cell Reception   Picnic Table

Good
Average
Poor

Gear & Supplies: _____

_____

Food & Beverages: _____

_____

Observances & Sightings (Nature, views, wildlife): _____

_____

Sketch/Photo/Notes

Sketch/Photo/Journal

Hike/Trail Name: _____

Date: _____ **Start Time:** _____ **End Time:** _____

City/State: _____ **Total Distance:** _____

Companions: _____

Trail Type: Loop   Out and Back   Point-to-point

Weather: ☀️ 🌤️ ☁️ 🌧️ ❄️

Difficulty/Grade of the Hike: (circle a grade level):

Grade—   1   2   3   4   5

Amenities: (check all that apply)

Drinking-Water   Pet Friendly   Toilets   Cell Reception (Good / Average / Poor)   Picnic Table

Gear & Supplies: _____

Food & Beverages: _____

Observances & Sightings (Nature, views, wildlife): _____

Sketch/Photo/Notes

Sketch/Photo/Journal

Hike/Trail Name: _____

Date: _____   Start Time: _____   End Time: _____

City/State: _____   Total Distance: _____

Companions: _____

Trail Type: Loop   Out and Back   Point-to-point

Weather: ☀ 🌤 ☁ 🌧 ❄

Difficulty/Grade of the Hike: (circle a grade level):

Grade—   1   2   3   4   5

Amenities: (check all that apply)

Drinking-Water   Pet Friendly   Toilets   Cell Reception (Good / Average / Poor)   Picnic Table

Gear & Supplies: _____

Food & Beverages: _____

Observances & Sightings (Nature, views, wildlife): _____

Sketch/Photo/Notes

Sketch/Photo/Journal

Hike/Trail Name: _____

Date: _____ **Start Time:** _____ **End Time:** _____

City/State: _____ **Total Distance:** _____

Companions: _____

Trail Type: Loop   Out and Back   Point-to-point

Weather: ☀ 🌤 ☁ 🌧 ❄

Difficulty/Grade of the Hike: (circle a grade level):

Grade—   1   2   3   4   5

Amenities: (check all that apply)

Drinking-Water   Pet Friendly   Toilets   Cell Reception   Picnic Table

Good
Average
Poor

Gear & Supplies: _____

Food & Beverages: _____

Observances & Sightings (Nature, views, wildlife): _____

Sketch/Photo/Notes

Sketch/Photo/Journal

Hike/Trail Name: _____

Date: _____   *Start Time:* _____   *End Time:* _____

City/State: _____   *Total Distance:* _____

Companions: _____

Trail Type: Loop   Out and Back   Point-to-point

Weather: ☀ 🌤 ☁ 🌧 ❄

Difficulty/Grade of the Hike: (circle a grade level):

Grade–   1   2   3   4   5

Amenities: (check all that apply)

Drinking-Water   Pet Friendly   Toilets   Cell Reception (Good / Average / Poor)   Picnic Table

Gear & Supplies: _____

_____

Food & Beverages: _____

_____

Observances & Sightings (Nature, views, wildlife): _____

_____

_____

Sketch/Photo/Notes

Sketch/Photo/Journal

Hike/Trail Name: _____

Date: _____   **Start Time:** _____   **End Time:** _____

City/State: _____   **Total Distance:** _____

Companions: _____

Trail Type: Loop   Out and Back   Point-to-point

Weather: ☼ ⛅ ☁ 🌧 ❄

Difficulty/Grade of the Hike: (circle a grade level):

Grade—   1   2   3   4   5

Amenities: (check all that apply)

Drinking-Water   Pet Friendly   Toilets   Cell Reception (Good Average Poor)   Picnic Table

Gear & Supplies: _____

Food & Beverages: _____

Observances & Sightings (Nature, views, wildlife): _____

Sketch/Photo/Notes

Sketch/Photo/Journal

Hike/Trail Name: _____

Date: _____ **Start Time:** _____ **End Time:** _____

City/State: _____ **Total Distance:** _____

Companions: _____

Trail Type: Loop   Out and Back   Point-to-point

Weather: ☼   ⛅   ☁   🌧   ❄

Difficulty/Grade of the Hike: (circle a grade level):

🚶   🧍‍♂️🦯   🧗

Grade—   1   2   3   4   5

Amenities: (check all that apply)

Drinking-Water   Pet Friendly   Toilets   Cell Reception (Good / Average / Poor)   Picnic Table

Gear & Supplies: _____

_____

Food & Beverages: _____

_____

Observances & Sightings (Nature, views, wildlife):

_____

_____

Sketch/Photo/Notes

Sketch/Photo/Journal

Hike/Trail Name: _____

Date: _____ **Start Time:** _____ **End Time:** _____

City/State: _____ **Total Distance:** _____

Companions: _____

Trail Type: Loop   Out and Back   Point-to-point

Weather: ☀   🌤   ☁   🌧   ❄

Difficulty/Grade of the Hike: (circle a grade level):

Grade—   1   2   3   4   5

Amenities: (check all that apply)

Drinking-Water   Pet Friendly   Toilets   Cell Reception   Picnic Table

Good / Average / Poor

Gear & Supplies: _____
_____

Food & Beverages: _____
_____

Observances & Sightings (Nature, views, wildlife):
_____
_____

Sketch/Photo/Notes

Sketch/Photo/Journal

Hike/Trail Name: _____

Date: _____ Start Time: _____ End Time: _____

City/State: _____ Total Distance: _____

Companions: _____

Trail Type: Loop Out and Back Point-to-point

Weather: ☼ ⛅ ☁ 🌧 ❄

Difficulty/Grade of the Hike: (circle a grade level):

Grade— 1 2 3 4 5

Amenities: (check all that apply)

Drinking-Water Pet Friendly Toilets Cell Reception (Good / Average / Poor) Picnic Table

Gear & Supplies: _____

Food & Beverages: _____

Observances & Sightings (Nature, views, wildlife): _____

Sketch/Photo/Notes

Sketch/Photo/Journal

Hike/Trail Name: _____

Date: _____   **Start Time:** _____   **End Time:** _____

City/State: _____   **Total Distance:** _____

Companions: _____

Trail Type: Loop   Out and Back   Point-to-point

Weather: ☀️   🌤️   ☁️   🌧️   ❄️

Difficulty/Grade of the Hike: (circle a grade level):

🚶   🧑‍🦯   🧗

Grade—   1   2   3   4   5

Amenities: (check all that apply)

Drinking-Water   Pet Friendly   Toilets   Cell Reception (Good / Average / Poor)   Picnic Table

Gear & Supplies: _____

_____

Food & Beverages: _____

_____

Observances & Sightings (Nature, views, wildlife):

_____

_____

Sketch/Photo/Notes

Sketch/Photo/Journal

Hike/Trail Name:

Date: *Start Time:*   *End Time:*

City/State: *Total Distance:*

Companions:

Trail Type: *Loop*   *Out and Back*   *Point-to-point*

Weather: ☼   ⛅   ☁   🌧   ❄

Difficulty/Grade of the Hike: (circle a grade level):

Grade—   1   2   3   4   5

Amenities: (check all that apply)

Drinking-Water   Pet Friendly   Toilets   Cell Reception   Good / Average / Poor   Picnic Table

Gear & Supplies:

Food & Beverages:

Observances & Sightings (Nature, views, wildlife):

Sketch/Photo/Notes

Sketch/Photo/Journal

Hike/Trail Name: _____

Date: _____ **Start Time:** _____ **End Time:** _____

City/State: _____ **Total Distance:** _____

Companions: _____

Trail Type: Loop   Out and Back   Point-to-point

Weather: ☀ ⛅ ☁ 🌧 ❄

Difficulty/Grade of the Hike: (circle a grade level):

Grade— 1   2   3   4   5

Amenities: (check all that apply)

Drinking-Water   Pet Friendly   Toilets   Cell Reception (Good / Average / Poor)   Picnic Table

Gear & Supplies: _____
_____

Food & Beverages: _____
_____

Observances & Sightings (Nature, views, wildlife):
_____
_____

Sketch/Photo/Notes

Sketch/Photo/Journal

Hike/Trail Name: _____

Date: _____   Start Time: _____   End Time: _____

City/State: _____   Total Distance: _____

Companions: _____

Trail Type: Loop   Out and Back   Point-to-point

Weather: ☀ 🌤 ☁ 🌧 ❄

Difficulty/Grade of the Hike: (circle a grade level):

Grade—   1   2   3   4   5

Amenities: (check all that apply)

Drinking-Water   Pet Friendly   Toilets   Cell Reception (Good / Average / Poor)   Picnic Table

Gear & Supplies: _____

Food & Beverages: _____

Observances & Sightings (Nature, views, wildlife): _____

Sketch/Photo/Notes

Sketch/Photo/Journal

Hike/Trail Name: _____

Date: _____ **Start Time:** _____ **End Time:** _____

City/State: _____ **Total Distance:** _____

Companions: _____

Trail Type: Loop   Out and Back   Point-to-point

Weather: ☀ 🌤 ☁ 🌧 ❄

Difficulty/Grade of the Hike: (circle a grade level):

Grade—   1   2   3   4   5

Amenities: (check all that apply)

Drinking-Water   Pet Friendly   Toilets   Cell Reception (Good / Average / Poor)   Picnic Table

Gear & Supplies: _____

Food & Beverages: _____

Observances & Sightings (Nature, views, wildlife): _____

Sketch/Photo/Notes

Sketch/Photo/Journal

Hike/Trail Name: _____

Date: _____ Start Time: _____ End Time: _____

City/State: _____ Total Distance: _____

Companions: _____

Trail Type: Loop   Out and Back   Point-to-point

Weather: ☀ 🌤 ☁ 🌧 ❄

Difficulty/Grade of the Hike: (circle a grade level):

Grade–   1   2   3   4   5

Amenities: (check all that apply)

Drinking-Water   Pet Friendly   Toilets   Cell Reception   Good / Average / Poor   Picnic Table

Gear & Supplies: _____

Food & Beverages: _____

Observances & Sightings (Nature, views, wildlife): _____

Sketch/Photo/Notes

Sketch/Photo/Journal

Hike/Trail Name: _____

Date: _____   **Start Time:** _____   **End Time:** _____

City/State: _____   **Total Distance:** _____

Companions: _____

Trail Type: Loop   Out and Back   Point-to-point

Weather: ☼ ⛅ ☁ 🌧 ❄

Difficulty/Grade of the Hike: (circle a grade level):

Grade—   1   2   3   4   5

Amenities: (check all that apply)

Drinking-Water   Pet Friendly   Toilets   Cell Reception (Good / Average / Poor)   Picnic Table

Gear & Supplies: _____

_____

Food & Beverages: _____

_____

Observances & Sightings (Nature, views, wildlife):

_____

_____

Sketch/Photo/Notes

Sketch/Photo/Journal

Hike/Trail Name: _____

Date: _____   *Start Time:* _____   *End Time:* _____

City/State: _____   *Total Distance:* _____

Companions: _____

Trail Type: Loop   Out and Back   Point-to-point

Weather: ☼   ⛅   ☁   🌧   ❄

Difficulty/Grade of the Hike: (circle a grade level):

Grade–   1   2   3   4   5

Amenities: (check all that apply)

Drinking-Water   Pet Friendly   Toilets   Cell Reception   Good Average Poor   Picnic Table

Gear & Supplies: _____

_____

Food & Beverages: _____

_____

Observances & Sightings (Nature, views, wildlife): _____

_____

_____

Sketch/Photo/Notes

Sketch/Photo/Journal

Hike/Trail Name: _____

Date: _____ **Start Time:** _____ **End Time:** _____

City/State: _____ **Total Distance:** _____

Companions: _____

Trail Type: Loop   Out and Back   Point-to-point

Weather: ☀   🌤   ☁   🌧   ❄

Difficulty/Grade of the Hike: (circle a grade level):

Grade—   1   2   3   4   5

Amenities: (check all that apply)

Drinking-Water   Pet Friendly   Toilets   Cell Reception Good / Average / Poor   Picnic Table

Gear & Supplies: _____

_____

Food & Beverages: _____

_____

Observances & Sightings (Nature, views, wildlife):

_____

_____

Sketch/Photo/Notes

Sketch/Photo/Journal

Hike/Trail Name: _____

Date: _____   **Start Time:** _____   **End Time:** _____

City/State: _____   **Total Distance:** _____

Companions: _____

Trail Type: Loop   Out and Back   Point-to-point

Weather: ☀ 🌤 ☁ 🌧 ❄

Difficulty/Grade of the Hike: (circle a grade level):

Grade—   1   2   3   4   5

Amenities: (check all that apply)

Drinking-Water   Pet Friendly   Toilets   Cell Reception (Good / Average / Poor)   Picnic Table

Gear & Supplies: _____

Food & Beverages: _____

Observances & Sightings (Nature, views, wildlife): _____

94

Sketch/Photo/Notes

Sketch/Photo/Journal

Hike/Trail Name: _____

Date: _____ **Start Time:** _____ **End Time:** _____

City/State: _____ **Total Distance:** _____

Companions: _____

Trail Type: Loop   Out and Back   Point-to-point

Weather: ☀️ 🌤️ ☁️ 🌧️ ❄️

Difficulty/Grade of the Hike: (circle a grade level):

Grade—   1   2   3   4   5

Amenities: (check all that apply)

Drinking-Water   Pet Friendly   Toilets   Cell Reception (Good / Average / Poor)   Picnic Table

Gear & Supplies: _____

Food & Beverages: _____

Observances & Sightings (Nature, views, wildlife): _____

Sketch/Photo/Notes

Sketch/Photo/Journal

Hike/Trail Name: _____

Date: _____ Start Time: _____ End Time: _____

City/State: _____ Total Distance: _____

Companions: _____

Trail Type: Loop   Out and Back   Point-to-point

Weather: ☀ 🌤 ☁ 🌧 ❄

Difficulty/Grade of the Hike: (circle a grade level):

Grade–   1   2   3   4   5

Amenities: (check all that apply)

Drinking-Water   Pet Friendly   Toilets   Cell Reception (Good / Average / Poor)   Picnic Table

Gear & Supplies: _____
_____

Food & Beverages: _____
_____

Observances & Sightings (Nature, views, wildlife): _____
_____
_____

Sketch/Photo/Notes

Sketch/Photo/Journal

Hike/Trail Name: _____

Date: _____   **Start Time:** _____   **End Time:** _____

City/State: _____   **Total Distance:** _____

Companions: _____

Trail Type: Loop   Out and Back   Point-to-point

Weather: ☀ ⛅ ☁ 🌧 ❄

Difficulty/Grade of the Hike: (circle a grade level):

Grade—   1   2   3   4   5

Amenities: (check all that apply)

Drinking-Water   Pet Friendly   Toilets   Cell Reception (Good / Average / Poor)   Picnic Table

Gear & Supplies: _____

Food & Beverages: _____

Observances & Sightings (Nature, views, wildlife): _____

Sketch/Photo/Notes

Sketch/Photo/Journal

Hike/Trail Name: _____

Date: _____ **Start Time:** _____ **End Time:** _____

City/State: _____ **Total Distance:** _____

Companions: _____

Trail Type: Loop Out and Back Point-to-point

Weather: ☀️ 🌤️ ☁️ 🌧️ ❄️

Difficulty/Grade of the Hike: (circle a grade level):

Grade— 1 2 3 4 5

Amenities: (check all that apply)

Drinking-Water Pet Friendly Toilets Cell Reception (Good / Average / Poor) Picnic Table

Gear & Supplies: _____

Food & Beverages: _____

Observances & Sightings (Nature, views, wildlife): _____

Sketch/Photo/Notes

Sketch/Photo/Journal

Hike/Trail Name: _____

Date: _____   **Start Time:** _____   **End Time:** _____

City/State: _____   **Total Distance:** _____

Companions: _____

Trail Type: Loop   Out and Back   Point-to-point

Weather: ☀ 🌤 ☁ 🌧 ❄

Difficulty/Grade of the Hike: (circle a grade level):

Grade—   1   2   3   4   5

Amenities: (check all that apply)

Drinking-Water   Pet Friendly   Toilets   Cell Reception (Good / Average / Poor)   Picnic Table

Gear & Supplies: _____

_____

Food & Beverages: _____

_____

Observances & Sightings (Nature, views, wildlife):

_____

_____

Sketch/Photo/Notes

Sketch/Photo/Journal

Hike/Trail Name: _____

Date: _____   Start Time: _____   End Time: _____

City/State: _____   Total Distance: _____

Companions: _____

Trail Type: Loop   Out and Back   Point-to-point

Weather: ☀ ⛅ ☁ 🌧 ❄

Difficulty/Grade of the Hike: (circle a grade level):

Grade—   1   2   3   4   5

Amenities: (check all that apply)

Drinking-Water   Pet Friendly   Toilets   Cell Reception (Good / Average / Poor)   Picnic Table

Gear & Supplies: _____

Food & Beverages: _____

Observances & Sightings (Nature, views, wildlife): _____

Sketch/Photo/Notes

Sketch/Photo/Journal

Hike/Trail Name: _____

Date: _____   **Start Time:** _____   **End Time:** _____

City/State: _____   **Total Distance:** _____

Companions: _____

Trail Type: Loop   Out and Back   Point-to-point

Weather: ☀️   🌤️   ☁️   🌧️   ❄️

Difficulty/Grade of the Hike: (circle a grade level):

Grade—   1   2   3   4   5

Amenities: (check all that apply)

Drinking-Water	Pet Friendly	Toilets	Cell Reception	Picnic Table

Cell Reception: Good / Average / Poor

Gear & Supplies: _____

Food & Beverages: _____

Observances & Sightings (Nature, views, wildlife): _____

Sketch/Photo/Notes

Sketch/Photo/Journal

Hike/Trail Name: _____

Date: _____ **Start Time:** _____ **End Time:** _____

City/State: _____ **Total Distance:** _____

Companions: _____

Trail Type: Loop   Out and Back   Point-to-point

Weather:

Difficulty/Grade of the Hike: (circle a grade level):

Grade–   1   2   3   4   5

Amenities: (check all that apply)

Drinking-Water   Pet Friendly   Toilets   Cell Reception   Picnic Table

Good
Average
Poor

Gear & Supplies: _____

_____

Food & Beverages: _____

_____

Observances & Sightings (Nature, views, wildlife): _____

_____

_____

Sketch/Photo/Notes

Sketch/Photo/Journal

Hike/Trail Name: _____

Date: _____   Start Time: _____   End Time: _____

City/State: _____   Total Distance: _____

Companions: _____

Trail Type: Loop   Out and Back   Point-to-point

Weather: ☀️ 🌤️ ☁️ 🌧️ ❄️

Difficulty/Grade of the Hike: (circle a grade level):

Grade–   1   2   3   4   5

Amenities: (check all that apply)

Drinking-Water   Pet Friendly   Toilets   Cell Reception (Good Average Poor)   Picnic Table

Gear & Supplies: _____
_____

Food & Beverages: _____
_____

Observances & Sightings (Nature, views, wildlife):
_____
_____

Sketch/Photo/Notes

Sketch/Photo/Journal

Hike/Trail Name: _____

Date: _____ Start Time: _____ End Time: _____

City/State: _____ Total Distance: _____

Companions: _____

Trail Type: Loop   Out and Back   Point-to-point

Weather: ☀ 🌤 ☁ 🌧 ❄

Difficulty/Grade of the Hike: (circle a grade level):

Grade—   1   2   3   4   5

Amenities: (check all that apply)

Drinking-Water   Pet Friendly   Toilets   Cell Reception Good / Average / Poor   Picnic Table

Gear & Supplies: _____

Food & Beverages: _____

Observances & Sightings (Nature, views, wildlife): _____

Sketch/Photo/Notes

Sketch/Photo/Journal

Hike/Trail Name: _____

Date: _____   **Start Time:** _____   **End Time:** _____

City/State: _____   **Total Distance:** _____

Companions: _____

Trail Type: Loop   Out and Back   Point-to-point

Weather: ☀ ⛅ ☁ 🌧 ❄

Difficulty/Grade of the Hike: (circle a grade level):

Grade—   1   2   3   4   5

Amenities: (check all that apply)

| Drinking-Water | Pet Friendly | Toilets | Cell Reception (Good, Average, Poor) | Picnic Table |

Gear & Supplies: _____

Food & Beverages: _____

Observances & Sightings (Nature, views, wildlife): _____

Sketch/Photo/Notes

Sketch/Photo/Journal

Hike/Trail Name: _____

Date: _____ **Start Time:** _____ **End Time:** _____

City/State: _____ **Total Distance:** _____

Companions: _____

Trail Type: Loop   Out and Back   Point-to-point

Weather: ☀ ⛅ ☁ 🌧 ❄

Difficulty/Grade of the Hike: (circle a grade level):

Grade–   1   2   3   4   5

Amenities: (check all that apply)

Drinking-Water   Pet Friendly   Toilets   Cell Reception (Good / Average / Poor)   Picnic Table

Gear & Supplies: _____

_____

Food & Beverages: _____

_____

Observances & Sightings (Nature, views, wildlife):

_____

_____

Sketch/Photo/Notes

Sketch/Photo/Journal

Hike/Trail Name: _____

Date: _____ **Start Time:** _____ **End Time:** _____

City/State: _____ **Total Distance:** _____

Companions: _____

Trail Type:　　Loop　　　　Out and Back　　　　Point-to-point

Weather:　☀　⛅　☁　🌧　❄

Difficulty/Grade of the Hike: (circle a grade level):

Grade—　　1　　　2　　　3　　　4　　　5

Amenities: (check all that apply)

Drinking-Water　　Pet Friendly　　Toilets　　Cell Reception (Good / Average / Poor)　　Picnic Table

Gear & Supplies: _____

_____

Food & Beverages: _____

_____

Observances & Sightings (Nature, views, wildlife):

_____

_____

Sketch/Photo/Notes

Sketch/Photo/Journal

Hike/Trail Name: _____

Date: _____   **Start Time:** _____   **End Time:** _____

City/State: _____   **Total Distance:** _____

Companions: _____

Trail Type: Loop   Out and Back   Point-to-point

Weather: ☀️ 🌤️ ☁️ 🌧️ ❄️

Difficulty/Grade of the Hike: (circle a grade level):

Grade–   1   2   3   4   5

Amenities: (check all that apply)

Drinking-Water   Pet Friendly   Toilets   Cell Reception (Good / Average / Poor)   Picnic Table

Gear & Supplies: _____

Food & Beverages: _____

Observances & Sightings (Nature, views, wildlife): _____

Sketch/Photo/Notes

Sketch/Photo/Journal

Hike/Trail Name: _____

Date: _____   **Start Time:** _____   **End Time:** _____

City/State: _____   **Total Distance:** _____

Companions: _____

Trail Type: Loop   Out and Back   Point-to-point

Weather: ☀   🌤   ☁   🌧   ❄

Difficulty/Grade of the Hike: (circle a grade level):

Grade—   1   2   3   4   5

Amenities: (check all that apply)

Drinking-Water   Pet Friendly   Toilets   Cell Reception (Good / Average / Poor)   Picnic Table

Gear & Supplies: _____

_____

Food & Beverages: _____

_____

Observances & Sightings (Nature, views, wildlife):

_____

_____

Sketch/Photo/Notes

Sketch/Photo/Journal

Notes

Notes

Thank you for choosing this journal!

Help us grow...

WE want to express our heartfelt gratitude to you, for helping us grow. We hope you enjoyed this journal and found it useful. Please consider telling a friend about this book. It would mean a world to us if you could leave an honest feedback about this journal on Amazon.com.

Thanks again for choosing to buy from a small business! We don't know what we would do, without you!